HBJ BOOKMARK READING PROGRAM

Margaret Early

Elizabeth K. Cooper

Nancy Santeusanio

Happy Morning

Stories by

Elizabeth K. Cooper

Stephen Mooser

Lin Oliver

Illustrations by Dora Leder

HARCOURT BRACE JOVANOVICH

New York   Chicago   San Francisco   Atlanta   Dallas   and   London

Contents

Requests for permission to make copies of any part of the work should be mailed to: Permissions; Harcourt Brace Jovanovich, Inc.; 757 Third Avenue; New York, New York 10017.

Printed in the United States of America   ISBN 0-15-331778-7

Friends

Kim sat in the sun.

Jack ran up.

Jack was Kim's friend.

And Kim was Jack's friend.

Jack said, "Good morning, Kim."

"Good morning, Jack," said Kim.

Jack sat down.
Kim got up.

6

Kim ran up to the hill.

Jack got up.

Jack ran after Kim.

The friends ran and ran in
the morning sun.

Down in the Grass

A wagon was in the grass.
"Jack," said Kim.
"A wagon!"

Jack went to the wagon.
And Jack said, "Junk!"

9

Kim said, "A wagon.
A good wagon."

Jack said, "Junk.
Junk lost in the grass."

Kim got in the wagon.

Kim said, "Can I fix
the wagon?

I can!

I can!"

The Friends Help

Kim went to fix the wagon.

Jack went to help.

And Kim's friends went to help.

Ted said, "I can fix the wagon."
Ted sat down in the grass.

Fay said, "I can help!
I can!"

Jack said, "Fay is little.
Can Fay help?"

Kim said, "Fay is not little.
Fay can help fix the wagon."

The friends sat down to help.

Kim said, "Good.

It is a good, good wagon."

A box was in the wagon.

Jack went to fix the box.

The box said

The Fix-it Wagon

The Fix-it Friends

The Little Cat

Ted ran up to the cat.

"Jump down, cat," said Ted.

The cat sat and sat.

Jack went up to Ted.
Ted said, "Jack, the cat is up.
It can not get down."

Jack said, "Get the fix-it wagon.
The fix-it wagon can help."

Ted went to get Kim and
the wagon.

Kim and Ted ran to the cat.

Kim said, "Get up in the wagon."

Ted jumped up.

But the little cat jumped away.

Ted said, "I can get the cat."
Ted went up and up.

Ted said, "Hop down.

Hop down, little lost cat."

The cat ran to Ted.

The cat jumped.

And Ted got the cat!

The Park

Fay met Kim.

The fix-it friends went to the park.

The park had grass.

It had a pond.

And it had junk.

Junk was in the park.

Junk was in the grass and
in the pond.

It was not a very good park.

Kim said, "The fix-it friends
can fix up the park."

Fay said, "Good.
Jack and Ted can help."

28

The Big Clean-up

Jack and Ted looked at the park.
Jack said, "It is a big, big
clean-up."

But Ted said, "Not to the
fix-it friends."

Kim had the fix-it wagon.

"I will clean the pond,"
said Kim.

Jack had a box.
It was a very big box.
"I will clean up the grass,"
said Jack.

Ted had a box.

"I will help Jack," said Ted.

Fay looked at the wagon.

"I will help Kim," said Fay.

The clean-up went on and on.
Ted said, "It **is** a big, big
clean-up, Jack."

"Look," said Fay.

"The fix-it friends cleaned up the park."

The grass was clean.

The pond was clean.

The park was clean.

The park looked very good.

The Wet, Wet Dog

It was a wet morning.

The park was wet.

The hill was wet.

The grass was wet.

And Casper was wet.

Casper was Jack's dog.

Kim and Jack went to Casper.

Kim had on a big hat.

Kim said, "Casper is very wet."

A box was in the wagon.

Jack got the box up on
Casper's house.

Kim had a hat.
And Casper's house had a hat!
Casper was not wet.
Casper was happy.

The Car in the Pond

Ted was at the pond.

Ted had a car.

The car went up and down.

The car went in the pond!
Down, down it went.
Ted looked in the pond.
"I lost the car!" said Ted.

Ted met Fay.

Fay had the fix-it wagon.

"Look," said Ted.

"The car is in the pond."

Fay said, "The fix-it wagon
will help."

A can was in the wagon.

A pipe was in the wagon.

Ted said, "The pipe and can
will help."

Ted got the can on the pipe.

Fay said, "Will the can and pipe
get the car?"

"The can and pipe will," said Ted.
Ted got the car.

Is It Lost?

The fix-it wagon was on the grass.

Mrs. Parks went up to it.

Mrs. Parks looked at the wagon.

"Is it junk?" said Mrs. Parks.

Mrs. Parks got the wagon up in
the car.

The fix-it friends ran up.

Kim said, "The wagon!
It is not here."

Ted said, "It was on the grass."

The fix-it wagon was lost!

Fay ran to the hill.
The wagon was not on the hill.

Ted ran to the park.
It was not in the park.

Kim ran in the house, and it
was not in the house.
The fix-it wagon was lost!

Jack met Mrs. Parks.

"Good morning," said Jack.

"I lost a wagon, Mrs. Parks."

Mrs. Parks said, "Look in the car, Jack."

Jack went to the car.

"Look!" said Jack.

"Here it is!"

It was a happy, happy morning.
The fix-it wagon was not lost!

The Dog Wash

Kim and Jack sat at the wagon.

"Dog wash," said Kim.

"Dogs washed here," said Jack.

Fay ran up to help.

Kim said, "Fay, can you get a
dog to wash?"

Fay said, "I can get a dog.
And I will."
Fay went to look.

Fay looked and looked.

And Fay got a dog.

It was Casper.

Casper was not very clean.

"You will look very good after
a wash, Casper," said Fay.

Casper at the Wash

"I got you a dog," said Fay.

"I got Casper."

Jack and Kim got up.

Jack looked at Casper.

"I can wash a big dog," said Jack.

"But not **so** big."

Casper ran and jumped at Jack.
Jack went down.

Casper ran to Kim.
"Get down, Casper!" said Kim.

Casper jumped on Fay.
Fay went down in the grass.

Casper jumped in the wagon.

The big dog sat in the wagon.

Casper was happy.

The fix-it wagon went down
the hill!

Kim and Jack ran after it.

But the wagon got away!

On and on went the wagon.

It went down, down, down the big hill.

It went up.

And it went down.

The wagon was in the pond.

And so was Casper!

Kim and Jack ran to the pond.

Kim said, "The fix-it friends
can wash big dogs.

Look at Casper!"

Casper was wet.

And Casper was clean.

Casper looked very, very good
after the wash.

The Band

"Look at the band," said Ted.
Kim looked.

Kim went to the fix-it wagon.
Kim got a pipe.
"I can play a pipe," said Kim.

Ted went to the wagon.

Ted said, "You can play?

So can I."

Fay went to the wagon.

"I will play a can," said Fay.

"And I will play on a box,"
said Jack.

The friends played.

Kim and Ted played pipes.

Fay played a can.

And Jack played a box.

It was a big, big band.

And it was a happy band!

Pipe and Play

The fix-it friends jumped up and ran,

And played on pipes, a box, a can.

The band went on and went away.

Play on, play on, Kim, Jack, Ted, Fay!

Pat Is Lost!

Look here!
Look here!
Mrs. Hill and the Little Cat!

Victor and Pat went to a big house.
On the house it said

Look here!
Look here!
Mrs. Hill and the Little Cat!

Victor and Pat went in.

Mrs. Hill said, "Good morning."

Mrs. Hill had a little cat.

"Look here!" said Mrs. Hill.

"4, 3, 2, 1!"

The little cat went away!
Victor said, "Mrs. Hill is very good."

Mrs. Hill looked down at Pat.
Mrs. Hill said, "Will you help?"
Pat ran up to Mrs. Hill.

Pat sat down on Mrs. Hill's wagon.

Mrs. Hill looked and looked at Pat.

Mrs. Hill jumped up and down.

Mrs. Hill said, "4, 3, 2, 1!"

And Pat went away!

Victor jumped up.

Victor ran up to Mrs. Hill.

Victor looked at Mrs. Hill.

"Pat is lost!" said Victor.

"Look here!" said Mrs. Hill.
"1, 2, 3, 4!"

The little cat was on the wagon.

And Pat was on the wagon.

Mrs. Hill was happy.

Pat was happy.

And so was Victor!